Franklin in Paris

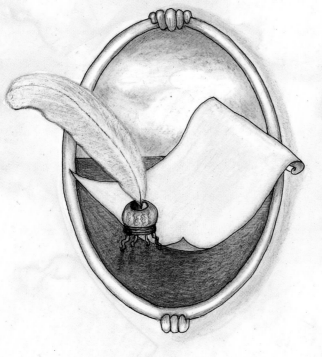

written by Ellie Mae Hudson

illustrated by Monica Passicot

Mc Graw Hill **Macmillan McGraw-Hill**

New York   Farmington

October 1776

My dearest Lucie,

We have had the most wonderful news! Benjamin Franklin, the great inventor, scientist, and wise man from Philadelphia, America, is coming here to Paris to see King Louis the Sixteenth! And I, as a page at King Louis's court, will have a chance to see the internationally famous Monsieur Franklin!

Everyone is getting excited about Monsieur Franklin's visit by reading and discussing his books. They also are wondering what he will look like. Some say he will be like a great lord and wear coats of the finest silk, while some think he will be like a professor and lecture everybody. I do not know what to expect for I have never seen an American before.

I will write to you soon, after I see the great Monsieur Franklin!

Your loving brother,
Jean-Pierre

December 1776
Dear Lucie,

You will not believe what happened when Monsieur Franklin arrived!

We waited in the courtyard for his coach. Monsieur Boulez yelled at all the pages that we were to be quiet and behave, but we were too excited to care. I held my breath as the coach door opened and here at last was the great Benjamin Franklin!

He was not at all what I expected. He wore a plain brown suit and he did not have a fancy powdered wig like the lords and ladies at court. He wore a simple black cloth hat, and he had on the bifocal eyeglasses he invented.

He stepped slowly out of the coach. Then Monsieur Boulez shouted, "Jean-Pierre! Come here and assist Monsieur Franklin!"

I ran over, bowed, then said in my best English, "Welcome to Paris, Monsieur Franklin!" And he smiled at me! Then he asked Monsieur Boulez if I could be his assistant while he was at court. Of course, Monsieur Boulez said yes. This is such a great honor! I will show him all around the city.

I cannot wait for the opportunity to talk more with Monsieur Franklin.

Your brother,
Jean-Pierre

January 1777
Dear Lucie,

I showed Monsieur Franklin around our beautiful palace of Versailles. I thought that he would enjoy seeing all the gold and marble and the fancy furniture, because they do not have anything like it in America. He admired the Hall of Mirrors, but I think he liked the gardens more. Then I showed him the little farm where Queen Marie Antoinette goes when she wants to relax and pretend that she is a simple peasant girl. Monsieur Franklin laughed and said that he did not think anyone would ever mistake the queen for a simple peasant girl!

Monsieur Franklin explained to me why
he has come to France to visit the king. He
says America needs help in its revolution for
freedom from English rule. America is a new
country and does not have as much money or
soldiers as England. He hopes that France
will send troops to help the American cause.

I wished Monsieur Franklin luck when he
went to speak with the king. But if he is
successful, and persuades the king to help,
he will sail back to the United States. I do
not want him to leave!

Your brother,
Jean-Pierre

February 1777

Dear Lucie,

I have wonderful news! The king has
agreed to help the Americans! And even
better, Monsieur Franklin is going to remain
in Paris a while longer so that he can
continue to represent America and its cause.
And I will remain his assistant.

Monsieur Franklin is the most talked—
about man in Paris. He goes to many parties,
and is much loved by everyone. The ladies
seem to be especially charmed by his
intellect and wit!

Monsieur Franklin is one of the kindest men I have ever met. We have long, interesting conversations about books, science, politics, and America. He does not treat me like a lowly servant, but talks to me like I am a friend. He says that is because there are no kings or royalty in America. Everyone is born equal. He is helping me to learn more English. Or is it American?

Monsieur Franklin now wants to find a place to live outside of the city. I hope he will take me with him!

Your brother,
Jean-Pierre

August 1777

Dear Lucie,

    Monsieur Franklin has found a lovely house in a town just outside of Paris. We looked at several places, and he asked my advice about which one to take. Monsieur Franklin has a beautiful estate here, with a large garden.

    Monsieur Franklin has told me about some of his scientific experiments. About thirty years ago, he did an experiment with a kite and key that proved that lightning was electricity. Maybe we can use the garden to try to catch lightning with a kite and a key again!

Monsieur Franklin plans to buy a printing press because he wants to be able to print his books or maybe a small newspaper. I look forward to learning how to use the printing press. He told me that when he was twelve, he was sent to live with his brother who was a printer. He became an apprentice, which is a kind of assistant, and he learned all about being a printer, but had to work long hours.

Monsieur Franklin has been elected to the Royal Medical Society of Paris. It seems that France cannot give him too many honors!

Your very busy brother,
Jean Pierre

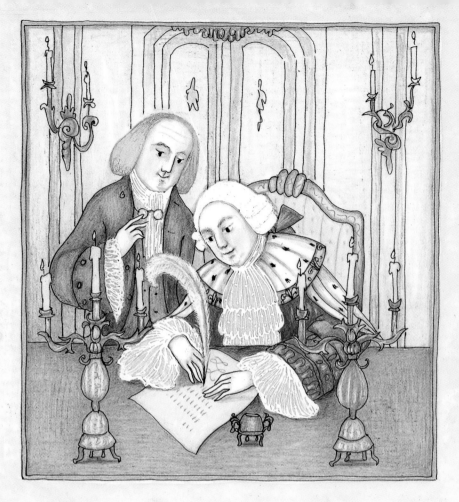

September 1778

Dear Lucie,

    Monsieur Franklin and I travel back and
forth to Paris a great deal. As you may have
heard, France is now officially fighting for the
Americans in their war against the British.
I am positive the reason is because of
Monsieur Franklin since he is so popular
that the king cannot refuse him anything!

Many people come to visit Monsieur Franklin at his home in the country and all the influential people in France want to meet him. Voltaire, our greatest French writer, comes to see him, and John Adams, the important American statesman, is now also in France. He visits Monsieur Franklin quite often and they have loud discussions about government and politics that can last almost all night! I am usually very tired, but I try to stay awake and listen to the two great Americans.

Your brother,
Jean-Pierre

December 1779
Dear Lucie,

It is hard to believe that I have been working with Monsieur Franklin for two years now. Mama and Papa tell me that I must return to court and continue my education there.

Yet I think I have had quite an education here. Monsieur Franklin has taught me to ask questions, and be curious, and to never stop learning from everything around me. My favorite thing was to assist him in his scientific experiments. Because of him, I think I would like to study science and maybe even become an inventor! I will miss him and his wise advice. He will always be my hero.

Your brother,
Jean-Pierre

January 1784

Dear Monsieur Franklin,

Thank you for your kind letter. I was glad to hear that you are well. I am well too. My studies are not easy, but I am working hard and I enjoy studying science, languages, and mathematics. There is so much to learn.

How amazing that you saw the first person ever to fly in a magnificent hot air balloon! And to think that they stayed afloat for ten whole minutes! Who knows what wonders we shall see next? Perhaps one day people will be able to soar and fly as easily as a bird does, but of course, I know that flight is impossible.

    I am glad that your war is over, and that
America and Britain are now at peace. I
know that you must soon return to
Philadelphia to help your new United States
of America. I wish you the best of luck, and I
hope that we will meet again. Maybe I will
come to visit you in Philadelphia in one of
the new magnificent hot air balloons!

Your friend always,
Jean Pierre